Be True

A Personal Guide to Becoming

Your Most Authentic Self

Julie Rosenberg, MD

Contents

A Letter to You

Dear Friend,

About ten years ago, I started really thinking about my life: Who I am. What motivates me. What's really important in my life. What I really want.

I thought I knew myself, but I realized that I was merely floating through life in a way that failed to bring me much meaning or value. As the product of an upper-middle-class family, I had always done what I thought I should do. I went to college, then medical school. I completed a medical internship, residency, and fellowship. I got married, secured a job, and started a family. I floated through these seemingly required steps but never took the time to embark on the deeper work of self-actualization or self-realization. It was through my practice of yoga and meditation that I became more introspective, more present, and better able to tolerate quiet moments. In those moments, I would listen to my thoughts and follow where my mind would go. My thoughts led me to understand that one of the things I loved most was writing. I saw writing not only as a creative outlet, but as a way to communicate and influence others by sharing ideas that could help support personal transformation.

As a result of that introspection, I wrote a book: *Beyond the Mat: Achieve Focus, Presence and Enlightened Leadership Through the Principles and Practice of Yoga*. My book uses those principles and practices to create a structure for optimal living and leading in modern times. In essence, my purpose in writing this book was to offer my readers a path to achieve their highest state of well-being.

Be True: A Personal Guide to Becoming Your Most Authentic Self takes the learnings from *Beyond the Mat* a step further, building upon lessons from my first book to offer a truly interactive learning experience. *Be True* is intended as a resource to both distill and extend the lessons from *Beyond the Mat*. I offer a framework to guide your contemplation and self-reflection and support you in your journey toward self-realization (knowing oneself) and self-actualization (the process of reaching your full potential).

While I recommend that you read *Beyond the Mat* to understand the framework of the yoga sutras and how they are as relevant today as they were in ancient India, it is not necessary to read it to work with *Be True*. Both *Beyond the Mat* and *Be True* offer ways in which you can develop greater focus, resilience, presence, and self-awareness to support your personal leadership journey and overall well-being.

One important note before we begin: This is meant to be a reflective process, so take your time. Don't complete the whole study guide in one sitting. Stop frequently. Reflect. Listen. Slowly find your way home.

I applaud you in taking this step to support yourself and to embark on a path to authenticity.

In gratitude,

Julie Rosenberg, MD

Introduction

"Yoga is the journey of the self, through the self, to the Self."
—*The Bhagavad Gita*

Our Western view of yoga is that it is a discipline composed of a series of pretzel-like physical exertions done to get fit and flexible, usually with some token Sanskrit words thrown in here and there. Yoga is an industry worth billions of dollars each year. The market is rife with swanky supplies and trendy clothing as well as exclusive yoga retreats in exotic places. A 2016 "Yoga in America" study conducted by *Yoga Journal* and Yoga Alliance showed that there are about 36 million active yogis in the United States and annual practitioner spending on yoga classes, clothing, equipment, and accessories was $16 billion—a $6 billion increase over the previous four years.

Yoga, however, is so much more.

Yoga may have entered the American mainstream as a tool for greater flexibility, fitness, and relaxation, but it goes well beyond the physical. The purpose of yoga is to cultivate discernment, self-awareness, self-regulation, and higher consciousness. Yoga is about how we live our lives in all contexts.

I myself turned to yoga sixteen years ago during a time of some personal and professional tumult. A professional shift from academic medicine to the pharmaceutical industry meant uprooting my life in Texas and relocating with my family to Connecticut. At the same time, my beloved father was diagnosed with advanced kidney cancer and died six months later. I felt helpless and, at times, hopeless. I turned to yoga on a whim and it was a decision that changed my life. Now, after more than a decade of serious practice, I find myself today with greater insight, clarity, and acuity. Yoga has helped me to become more grounded as a person, and its profound, far-reaching philosophies have shaped my thinking and especially my attitude toward working in the corporate world. It was the way that I came to truly know myself.

Svadhyaya is a virtuous observance in the practice of yoga, connoting introspection and "study of self." The word itself is comprised of *sva*, meaning "own" or "self," and *adhyaya*, meaning "lesson." By studying the self and recognizing our habits and thought processes, we can see which of our thoughts and actions may not be aligned with who we really are—our authentic self. We become more aware of our actions and the things we do that harm ourselves. We also become more aware of those thoughts and actions that serve us and bring us closer to a union with our true Self. In fact, the word "yoga" is actually derived from the Sanskrit root word *yuj* which means "union" or "oneness." Therefore, yoga is the union of the body, mind, and spirit.

My goal in offering this guide is to help you in cultivating the practice of *svadhyaha* and applying it to your modern-day life—to situations that you are in *right now*.

Stephen Cope, Scholar-in-Residence and Ambassador at Kripalu, offers an excellent distillation of the principle: "*Svadhyaya* is a skillful and systematic investigation of how things are. When you practice self-observation, you begin to uncover and address the unconscious patterns governing your life." When you notice—rather than judge—you develop empathy for yourself and gain the stability necessary to extend that empathy to others.

Knowing what you're doing in each moment requires you to be fully present and to pay close attention—to ask the question, *Why am I doing this?* Through *svadhyaha*, you will learn to recognize your habits and to discern between the ones which come from an ego-based place and which are the result of listening to your own wisdom—the wisdom of your true self. You will learn to observe yourself, almost as if you were watching someone else. And, importantly, you will learn to observe yourself without judgement. Through being present and learning to accept "what is," we learn to accept ourselves and to welcome ourselves as we are.

Be True will support you in contemplation and reflection so that you can build the skills to become your authentic self. The concept of "your authentic self" is more than a buzzword. When you discover your authentic self, you will be happier and experience a greater sense of well-being.

Let's begin this journey together.

The Eight Limbs of Yoga

The eight limbs of Ashtanga yoga map the journey one takes when studying and practicing yoga. The eight limbs support an aspirant in drawing his or her consciousness from an external focus to an internal focus. The Yoga Sutras of Patañjali are the 196 Indian sutras, or aphorisms, that the Hindu scholar Patañjali compiled from even older traditions. According to Patañjali, the right means are as important as the end goal. He enumerates these means as the eight limbs, or stages, of yoga for the quest of the soul.

The eight-fold path of yoga involves the following steps:

1. *Yama* (universal moral commandments; good conduct)
2. *Niyama* (self-purification by discipline; living in grace)
3. *Asana* (posture)
4. *Pranayama* (rhythmic control of breath)

5. *Pratyahara* (withdrawal and liberation of the mind from the domination of the senses and exterior objects; directing our attention internally)

6. *Dharana* (one-pointed concentration, as our minds can only truly focus on one thing at a time)

7. *Dhyana* (meditation)

8. *Samadhi* (the highest stage in meditation, in which a person experiences oneness with the universe)

Both *Beyond the Mat* and *Be True* are organized so that they utilize the eight limbs of yoga as a structure for learning and self-reflection. One notable exception is that *Be True* does not focus on *asana*.

1. Identifying Your Core Values

"Effectiveness without values is a tool without a purpose."
—Edward de Bono

Core values are traits or qualities that represent our most deeply held beliefs and highest priorities. They are principles and standards that guide our behavior, decisions, and actions. Our core values form the foundation of our character and influence how we lead our lives.

Below are 75 common core values:

Achievement	Adaptability	Adaptability
Altruism	Ambition	Assertiveness

Balance	Boldness	Brilliance
Calm	Candor	Commitment
Compassion	Competence	Contentment
Courage	Creativity	Curiosity
Decisiveness	Determination	Devotion
Dignity	Drive	Empathy
Endurance	Equality	Ethics
Excellence	Fearlessness	Focus
Fortitude	Freedom	Generosit
Grace	Gratitude	Greatness
Growth	Happiness	Health
Honesty	Hope	Humility
Integrity	Intelligence	Intuition
Joy	Kindness	Leadership
Learning	Love	Motivation
Openness	Optimism	Passion
Patience	Peace	Playfulness
Poise	Power	Productivity
Prosperity	Purpose	Reflection
Self-reliance	Serenity	Solitude
Spirituality	Success	Tranquility
Trust	Truth	Uniqueness
Vision	Wealth	Wisdom

With these 75 common core values in mind (and feel free to add others of your own), take a moment to reflect. Ask yourself: *What's most important in my life? What must I have in my life to experience fulfillment?* Write down five to ten values that are really important to you and then, on a scale of 1 to 10 (where 10 represents optimally living the value), rank how you are presently honoring each value in your life. Take some time to reflect. Remember, there are no right or wrong answers.

Value	Rank (1 – 10)
1.	
2.	
3.	
4.	
5.	
6.	
7.	
8.	
9.	
10.	

Now write about what your chosen values mean to you. Different words mean different things to different people, so take some time to define what each value means to you.

Value	Meaning
1.	
2.	
3.	
4.	
5.	
6.	
7.	
8.	
9.	
10.	

Once you have your core values written down and put in a safe place, choose a day and time each week for the next several months to regularly review them. This brief exercise will help you to internalize them. Authentic individuals live in alignment with their highest core values.

2. Living a Purposeful Life

"The secret of happiness: Find something more important than you
are and dedicate your life to it."
—Daniel C. Dennett

We are all meant to shine. But in order to really shine and prosper, we need to find purpose. At one time or another, we all ask the question, "Why am I here?" We need to answer that question in order to find our purpose.

Purpose is not a job, role, title, or a cause. Purpose is not focused on outcomes. Purpose:

- Works in all aspects of your life.
- Defines success for you and what really matters to you.

- Embraces your uniqueness.
- Reflects your passions and core values.

The first step to finding your purpose is self-evaluation. Spend a few moments thinking about the unique talents and gifts you bring to the world. Then spend a few minutes thinking about what a meaningful life means to you. Contemplate and write a few sentences as to what you want your future to look like.

_____

_____

_____

_____

_____

_____

_____

_____

_____

The next step is solidifying that self-evaluation with a personal purpose statement. The statement is meant to explain precisely who you aim to be. It will be the guiding principle behind how you spend your time and energy and how you steer your life. The more consistent your actions are with your personal purpose, the more authentic your life will be.

As an example, since my life's work is focused on defining and implementing creative ways to support and advance the well-being of all people, my personal purpose statement is: "To be a vital force in the advancement of global well-being." In my statement, I am true to myself and I define the impact of my service to others.

TRY THIS IN TWO MINUTES: REFLECT ON PURPOSE

Imagine that you are 100 years old. Reflect back on your life. Let your thoughts wander initially and then focus on the following three questions. Your answers will help you in defining your purpose.

What one thing did you accomplish that made you the most proud?

_____

_____

_____

_____

_____

_____

_____

_____

Who did you serve?

What was the impact?

To help guide development of your personal purpose statement, ask yourself these five questions:

Who am I? (character)

_____

_____

_____

_____

_____

_____

_____

_____

_____

What do I do? (mission)

_____

_____

_____

_____

_____

_____

_____

_____

_____

Who do I do it for? (community)

_____

_____

_____

_____

_____

_____

_____

What do they want or need? (service)

_____

_____

_____

_____

_____

_____

_____

_____

How are they changed? (impact)

_____

_____

_____

_____

_____

_____

_____

_____

Use words that reflect positive action instead of merely focusing on what you want to avoid. Your words should reflect who you are and what you want to bring to the world. Don't overthink or overanalyze your statement. Don't judge what you have written. Remember that your personal purpose statement is a work in process. You can step away and return to it until you have written words that clearly reflect what you want to express.

Write your personal purpose statement here:

_____

_____

_____

_____

_____

_____

_____

_____

_____

_____

_____

_____

_____

_____

_____

_____

_____

_____

_____

_____

_____

_____

_____

_____

_____

Now that you have written your personal purpose statement, moving through this guide will support you in leading a more a purposeful life. The next steps are two-fold. First, you must take a close look at yourself and do a full self-assessment: Where are you at this very moment on that journey to a morer purposeful life? How much of your life has been lived until this point with that purpose in mind? Next, you must commit to making that life happen. You must be willing to live your truth, rather than living a life that you think others want you to have. When you learn to abandon external pressures and move in accordance with your own personal compass, you will be able to live an authentic and purposeful life.

Note: Your purpose may change over time with shifting values. Revisit your work at least once per year.

3. Building Your Personal Foundation

"Discontent, blaming, complaining, self-pity cannot serve as a foundation for a good future, no matter how much effort you make."
—Eckhardt Tolle

I n the yoga sutras of Patañjali, the first of the eight limbs of yoga are the *yamas*, universal moral and ethical commandments for "right living." They are guidelines for how we can best show up for our lives, and they apply broadly to our actions, words, and thoughts. I have come to see the *yamas* as an essential foundation for sustainable success in life.

> The *Yamas*
>
> *Ahimsa*—nonviolence / compassion
>
> *Satya*—truth
>
> *Asteya*—nonstealing
>
> *Brahmacharya*—control of the senses
>
> *Aparigraha*—to take only what is necessary

The *yamas* are broken down into five "wise characteristics." On the surface, these five wise characteristics may sound familiar to those of us in the West: don't commit violence (*ahimsa*), tell the truth (*satya*), don't steal what others have (*asteya*), practice self-restraint (*brahmacharya*), and take only what is necessary (*aparigraha*). But unlike our more commonly understood set of rules—the Ten Commandments—the *yamas* go deeper as rules of morality for society and individuals. Rather than a list of dos and don'ts, the *yamas* aim to help practitioners develop a powerful set of interpersonal skills, from patience to fearlessness.

AHIMSA: NON-VIOLENCE/COMPASSION

Ahimsa literally means not to injure or show cruelty to any living being. However, more than the literal interpretation of nonviolence, it implies that in every situation, we should adopt a kind, thoughtful, and considerate attitude and that we should exercise compassion.

Negative thoughts are a form of violence. Write down your three most negative thoughts.

1.
_____
_____
_____
_____
_____
_____
_____
_____

2.
_____
_____
_____
_____
_____
_____
_____
_____

3.

_____

_____

_____

_____

_____

_____

_____

_____

Come back to these at a later time and observe them. The act of observing this negativity rather than being mired in it helps help you to stop feeding these negative thoughts and supports your ultimate liberation from them.

Do your thoughts, actions and words come from a place of compassion?

Yes ☐   No ☐

_____

_____

_____

_____

_____

_____

_____

_____

_____

What attitudes do you have that might be keeping you from feeling at peace?

_____

_____

_____

_____

_____

_____

_____

_____

What acts or gestures of kindness did you offer recently? How did they make you feel?

_____

_____

_____

_____

_____

_____

_____

_____

_____

How can you live and lead your life with greater compassion? With greater peace?

_____

_____

_____

_____

_____

_____

_____

_____

What do you need to change to achieve these desired outcomes?

_____

_____

_____

_____

_____

_____

Sit in an upright position. Create an intention for peace in your life. Take ten deep breaths. Inhale and exhale each to a count of five. On the exhale, say the word "peace" silently to yourself. After your tenth full cycle of breath, check in with yourself and see how you feel. Are you more at ease? More peaceful?

SATYA: TRUTH

The principle of *Satya*, the Sanskrit word for truth, is based on the understanding that honest communication and action form the foundation of healthy relationships and societies. *Satya* requires that we consider what we say, how we say it, and in what way it could impact others. In other words, truth encompasses our thoughts, speech, and actions.

CONTEMPLATION AND JOURNALING

What does truth mean to you?

_____

_____

_____

_____

_____

_____

_____

Are your words and actions truthful?

Yes ☐   No ☐

_____

_____

_____

_____

_____

_____

_____

_____

Are you truthful with yourself?

Yes ☐   No ☐

_____

_____

_____

_____

_____

_____

_____

_____

How do you feel when you have not been truthful?

_____

_____

_____

_____

_____

_____

_____

What has been the effect on others?

_____

_____

_____

_____

_____

_____

_____

_____

_____

_____

ASTEYA: DON'T STEAL

The Sanskrit word *steya* means to steal. *Asteya* is the opposite: to take nothing that does not belong to us. *Asteya* also means that if we are in a situation in which someone entrusts something to us or confides in us, we should not take advantage of him or her. Nonstealing includes not only not taking what belongs to another without permission but also not using something for a different purpose other than for what it is intended or beyond the time permitted by its owner. The practice of *asteya* implies not taking *anything* that has not been freely given. This includes being conscious of how we ask for others' time since demanding another's attention when not freely given is, in effect, stealing.

Do you pay equal attention to what you are contributing and to your own needs in every situation?

Yes ☐   No ☐

_____

_____

_____

_____

_____

_____

_____

Do you respect the time and energy of others?

Yes ☐   No ☐

_____

_____

_____

_____

_____

_____

_____

_____

_____

Are you mindful of what you are taking in each situation that you encounter, both literally and metaphorically?

Yes ☐   No ☐

_____

_____

_____

_____

_____

_____

_____

_____

BRAHMACHARYA: CONTROL OF THE SENSES

Brahmacharya has often been interpreted literally as celibacy, but it actually means "living in divine consciousness." *Brahma* literally means the "divine consciousness," and *charya*, in this context, means "living" or "one who is established in." In simple terms, *brahmacharya* means control

34

of the senses or living in moderation. Living in *brahmacharya* means control over impulses of excess, such as food, sex, gambling, shopping—anything in which we may indulge.

CONTEMPLATION AND JOURNALING

Is your behavior driven by urges, such as eating large amounts of food when you're not really hungry or drinking too much alcohol?

Yes ☐   No ☐

_____

_____

_____

_____

_____

_____

_____

_____

_____

Do you continually strive for more in your life?

Yes ☐   No ☐

_____

_____

_____

_____

_____

_____

_____

_____

When and how will you know that you have enough?

_____

_____

_____

_____

_____

_____

_____

_____

APARIGRAHA: TO TAKE ONLY WHAT IS NECESSARY

We often find ourselves wanting. *Aparigraha* means to take only what is necessary—not to hoard or accumulate goods through greed. *Aparigraha* also implies non-possessiveness or letting go of our attachments to things as well as our need to control people or our surroundings.

CONTEMPLATION AND JOURNALING

Is your life cluttered? If so, how?

_____

_____

_____

_____

_____

_____

_____

_____

What are you holding on to (or clinging to) in your life? Can you let it go?

_____

_____

How can you live more simply?

Make a list of five positive characteristics that you have. Spend a moment recognizing and celebrating yourself. You will feel less jealous or envious of others when you take time to bathe in your own brilliance.

1. _____

2. _____

3. _____

4. _____

5. _____

4. Personal Growth

"You cannot dream yourself into a character;
you must hammer and forge yourself one."
—Henry David Thoreau

The second of the eight limbs of yoga, *niyama*, literally means positive duties or observances. The *niyamas* are five personal practices—cleanliness (*saucha*), contentment (*santosha*), self-restraint (*tapas*), self-study (*svadhyaya*), and devotion *(Ishvara Pranidhana)*—that describe how we should act toward ourselves and encourage us to live and work with self-discipline.

SAUCHA: CLEANLINESS

Saucha, translated as "purification" or "cleanliness," is a clearing out on all levels. *Saucha* means cleanliness of body, mind, spirit, and surroundings. Practicing *saucha* leads us toward a pure and positive life. *Saucha* is equivalent to self-care.

CONTEMPLATION AND JOURNALING

The state of our environment often reflects the state of our mind.

Do you strive to keep your body, clothing, food, home, and work environment clean? Are you keeping your life clean and pure?

Yes ☐   No ☐

_____

_____

_____

_____

_____

_____

_____

Are you breathing freely and effortlessly? (The breath helps to cleanse us of toxins that have built up in the body and mind).

Yes ☐   No ☐

_____

_____

_____

_____

_____

_____

_____

_____

Are you making conscious choices about the foods that you eat? Are you eating high-quality, unrefined, and minimally processed foods such as vegetables and fruits, whole grains, healthy fats, and good sources of protein?

Yes ☐   No ☐

_____

_____

_____

_____

_____

_____

_____

_____

_____

Are your motives unselfish?

Yes ☐   No ☐

_____

_____

_____

_____

_____

_____

_____

_____

_____

Are you comfortable with yourself? Can you just be yourself without pretense?

Yes ☐   No ☐

Are you comfortable spending time in solitude?

Yes ☐   No ☐

_____

_____

_____

Santosha: Contentment

Santosha means contentment—being satisfied with what you have and who you are— in the present moment. Most of us have been taught to believe that contentment is linked to our accomplishments or constantly getting more. Our basic value is that "more is better," and we place a variety of personal qualifications on our contentment. For example, we think, *I'll be content when I get a different job, a bigger home or a new car,* etc. Contentment is gratitude, appreciation, and acceptance *for the way things are now.*

Contemplation and Journaling

When in your life do you recall being the most content?

_____

_____

_____

_____

_____

_____

_____

Describe the environment in which you are most content.

How often do you take a moment to notice "what is" and accept it?

Are there areas of your life in which you're not content?

Yes ☐   No ☐

_____

_____

_____

_____

_____

_____

_____

_____

_____

What are 3 things you can do today to feel more grateful and/or more content?

1.

_____

_____

_____

_____

_____

_____

_____

2.

3.

48

TAPAS: SELF-DISCIPLINE

The word *tapas* is derived from the Sanskrit verb *tap*, which means to burn. *Tapas* has traditionally been interpreted to mean "fiery discipline." We use it to focus our energy, create fervor, and increase strength and confidence. Self-discipline is your ability to control your desires, emotions, impulses, and behaviors to stay focused on what needs to get done to successfully meet your goals.

CONTEMPLATION AND JOURNALING

Why is self-discipline important in your life?

_____

_____

_____

_____

_____

_____

_____

_____

_____

_____

Do you hold yourself accountable at home? At work?

At home: At work:

Yes ☐   No ☐   Yes ☐   No

For what do you hold yourself accountable at home? At work?

In what areas would you like to improve your self-discipline? (Examples: Making decisions, overcoming procrastination, completing tasks, persevering).

_____

_____

_____

_____

_____

_____

_____

_____

_____

TRY THIS IN TWO MINUTES: DISCIPLINE YOURSELF

Self-discipline is a learned behavior. Think about two areas of your life in which you would like have more self-discipline. Write down your goals for each area. How do you plan to achieve them? If you break your goals into small steps instead of trying to change everything at once, these consistent efforts will help you to master self-discipline through meaningful habit change. For example, if you want to begin an exercise program, start with 15-20 minutes per day and work up to 50-60 minutes per day.

Goal 1:

_____

_____

_____

_____

_____

_____

_____

_____

My plan to achieve Goal 1:

_____

_____

_____

_____

_____

_____

_____

_____

Goal 2:

_____

_____

_____

_____

_____

_____

_____

My plan to achieve Goal 2:

_____

_____

_____

_____

_____

_____

_____

_____

SVADHYAYA: SELF-STUDY

Svadhyaya means to remember, contemplate, or meditate on the self. *Svadhyaya* is the practice of rigorous and honest self-inquiry and self-examination, which leads to greater self-awareness. As the Greek philosopher Aristotle said, "Knowing yourself is the beginning of all wisdom." However, it must be noted that contemplation is merely the first step. It must be followed up with a more active self-examination process. As Dr. Tasha Eurich, author of *Insight: Why We're Not as Self-Aware as We Think, and How Seeing Ourselves Clearly Helps Us Succeed at Work and in Life*, states, "True insight only happens when we process both our thoughts and our feelings."

CONTEMPLATION AND JOURNALING

Who are you today?

_____

_____

_____

_____

_____

_____

_____

_____

_____

Who do you want to be?

_____

_____

_____

_____

_____

_____

_____

_____

If you could do anything now, what would it be?

_____

_____

_____

_____

_____

_____

_____

_____

_____

What's holding you back from just doing that thing?

_____

_____

_____

_____

_____

_____

_____

_____

What does happiness mean for you?

_____

_____

_____

_____

_____

_____

_____

_____

_____

What do you like about yourself?

_____

_____

_____

_____

_____

_____

_____

What are you self-conscious or insecure about?

_____

_____

_____

_____

_____

_____

_____

_____

_____

If today were your last day, how would you spend it? Who would you spend it with? Where would you go?

_____

_____

_____

_____

_____

_____

_____

After your death, how would you like to be remembered? What will your legacy be? How does this impact you now?

_____

_____

_____

_____

_____

_____

_____

ISHVARA PRANIDHANA: DEVOTION OR SURRENDER TO A HIGHER SOURCE

Very often *ishvara* is taken to mean "God," but it is really your personal approach to the divine. It's your choice to connect with whatever resonates personally with you. It may be God, Jesus, Buddha, or the experience in nature or the appreciation of music. *Ishvara* may have a personal meaning for you that does not resonate with anyone else. *Pranidhana* is devotion or surrender. Put together, *ishvara pranidhana* is an attitude of devotion you carry with you and with which you live your life. Taking this concept a step further, being true requires letting go of the ego in order to manifest the divine.

In our daily lives, *Isvara Pranishana* can be seen as less of a surrendering and more of an 'opening up to 'what is.' By this I mean that instead of fighting against the ups and downs of our lives, we remain open to experiencing our life as it unfolds.

CONTEMPLATION AND JOURNALING

How do you conceive of the divine?

_____

_____

_____

_____

Do you incorporate a sense of spirituality into your life?

Yes ☐   No ☐

_____

_____

_____

_____

_____

_____

_____

_____

If yes, in what way are your contributions more meaningful and fulfilling as a spiritual being?

_____

_____

_____

_____

5. The Power of Breath

"Every breath is new, and every breath brings us into the present moment. The breath is the metronome of now."
—Jillian Pransky

In Sanskrit, *prana* means breath. More fundamentally, it means energy, strength, vitality—the life force that holds all things together. *Pranayama* connotes the expansion of breath and its control and fosters the development of breath as a tool for vital living. It is a specific, intentional way of inhaling and exhaling over a period of time to produce a desired effect on your body and mind. The aim of *pranayama* is to foster a free and undisturbed flow of *prana* so we can quiet and calm our minds and focus successfully on the task at hand.

In today's society, most of us live and work in conditions in which we experience chronic stress. Untreated chronic stress can result in serious health conditions including anxiety, depression, insomnia, high blood pressure, poor digestion, and a weakened immune system, to name a few.

When we are stressed or fearful, we often have difficulty catching our breath, feel like our breathing is labored, or find ourselves gasping for air. Such breathing patterns can activate the sympathetic nervous system, often referred to as the fight-or-flight response. *Pranayama* is meant to expand, intensify, and consolidate the energies of the breath by directing, regulating, and balancing their flow. This process helps us break our unconscious breathing patterns and make our breath long, easeful, and smooth.

Deep breathing is one of the most efficient ways to focus on the present, center yourself, and feel relaxed, thereby reducing stress and anxiety even in the most challenging moments. When you breathe deeply, it sends a very clear message to your brain: Calm down and relax.

Take a moment to sit quietly and check in with your breath with these five steps:

1. Observe your breath without the intention of changing it. Be aware if the breath is changing anyway. Just be aware. Don't manipulate. Just observe.
2. Where do you feel your breathing? Is there a part of your body where your breath is more noticeable?

3. What is the quality of your breathing? Is it smooth or rough, easy or labored, jerky or rhythmic, deep or shallow?
4. What is the pace of your breathing? Fast or slow?
5. Now gently close your eyes and breathe deeply and slowly in and out through your nose, for a few minutes. Do you feel a release from tension, pain, or stress? What has shifted for you?

Just observing your breath for few minutes can have a calming influence.

TRY THIS IN TWO MINUTES: DEEP DIAPHRAGMATIC BREATHING

The basic mechanics of deep diaphragmatic breathing include three parts. First, inhale deeply through the nose for a count of five or so, making sure the abdomen rises and feeling the lower ribs expand against your hand. Next, hold the breath for three to five seconds before exhaling completely through the mouth for a count longer than the inhalation. Once your lungs are empty and your belly is contracted, repeat the cycle.

Complete seven to ten cycles. Your goal is to breathe three-dimensionally, expanding on all sides and aiming your breath toward your back as well as your front. This brings a feeling of being centered along the axis of your spine, and your attention will be drawn inward with the breath.

Try this hourly or, if that's too daunting, start by trying it at random moments throughout your day. Remember: What I have described takes just two minutes, and you will likely find in even that short time that your overall stress level is much improved and that you feel more grounded. Practing slow, deep breathing will induce the parasympathetic response, which supports relaxation and counteracts stress.

6. Conquering Distractions

"By prevailing over all obstacles and distractions, one may
unfailingly arrive at his chosen goal or destination."
—Christopher Columbus

In today's world, doing one thing at a time is no longer enough. Most
of us practice multitasking, and it is ingrained in our daily lives—we
are constantly texting, writing emails, checking Facebook, talking on the
phone, listening to podcasts, catching up on the news. We think we are
being efficient, but the reality is that the constant interruption and
distraction that comes from multitasking disrupts our ability to stay
focused and present. Brain researchers say that what many people call
multitasking should really be called "rapid toggling" between tasks, as
the brain focuses quickly on one topic, then switches to another, and
another. It then takes time to re-immerse your mind in the point of focus.

We all have constant mind chatter in our daily lives. Our "monkey minds" typically jump in and out throughout the day with a running commentary—we find ourselves judging, critiquing, and assigning meaning to things that don't need our constant attention. We have an "always on" digital culture and find ourselves constantly stimulated by the immediacy of technology.

We must make a conscious effort to draw our awareness away from the external world and outside stimuli. When we focus our attention, we learn to separate relevant information from irrelevant information, allowing for conscious, nonreactive decision making.

TRY THIS IN TWO MINUTES: PAUSE

It's easy to get caught up in the frenetic pace of each day. Here is a simple exercise (and one of my favorites) that you can perform in two minutes or less to help you implement the lessons of the *yamas* in order to deliver a more mindful, compassionate, truthful, and powerful response.

Prior to speaking, take a breath, *pause,* and ask yourself:

    Is it true?

    Is it necessary?

    Is it timely?

    Is it helpful?

    Can it be said with compassion?

CONTEMPLATION AND JOURNALING

Constant interruptions are akin to multitasking. Do you establish boundaries at work? At home?

At home: At work:

Yes ☐   No ☐   Yes ☐   No ☐

_____

_____

_____

_____

_____

_____

_____

_____

Do you take breaks throughout the day to allow yourself to rest and regain energy by stepping away from your work or the task at hand?

Yes ☐   No ☐

_____

_____

_____

_____

_____

_____

_____

_____

_____

How much time do you spend on electronic devices each day? Do you put your technology devices away to allow yourself more space—both mental and physical—to work?

_____

_____

_____

_____

_____

_____

_____

_____

If you stop multitasking, you will accomplish more in less time. Try these tips to conquer distractions:

- **Clear clutter**. Having a clean, organized personal space can reduce stress levels and lead to better engagement throughout the day.

- **Do a time audit.** Learn the major sources of your distractions. Email? Text messages? Twitter? Your boss? Log your time for a week in a spreadsheet, journal, or whatever works for you. Consider using a time tracker to determine how much time you spend on apps and websites.

- **Avoid multi-tasking.** Our brains cannot do two things at once – we are actually task-switching which leads to decreased productivity.

- **Take regular-timed breaks throughout each day.** Every hour or two, take a five- or ten-minute break when possible. Go for a short walk, read a book, or listen to music. This can improve productivity and help you to be more focused.

- **First thing in the morning, work on your most important task.** Keep focused until this task is complete.

- **Block out background noise.** Consider wearing noise-canceling headphones or playing white noise to block out external stimuli that are competing for your attention.

- **Don't get hung up on your phone.** Get some physical distance from your phone. Leave it in another room or put it in a drawer or box that isn't within arm's length.

- **Be intentional about time management.** Time is one of our most precious commodities. Be intentional with it. Devise a time management approach that divides the available time into categories and ensures that your focus and emphasis are on the highest-value items.

TRY THIS IN TWO MINUTES: RE-FOCUS

When you get the urge to check your email, phone or switch to another task, stop yourself for a moment. Breathe deeply, inhaling and exhaling each to a count of five. Re-focus yourself while completing eight cycles of breath. Get back to the primary task at hand.

7. Learning to Be Present

"There is only one time that is important—NOW!
It is the most important time because
it is the only time that we have any power."
—Leo Tolstoy

So much of our time is spent brooding about the past or worrying about the future rather than living in the present moment. What if we could just let it be? In other words, what if we could just be with ourselves and savor what is?

It's difficult for most of us to stay in the present moment. Distractions are a way of life. Switching off from both internal and external distractions is not easy. However, greater ease and happiness are found by being present and mindful. Being present also improves your focus and helps you tune out background distractions and noise.

How do we develop our mind's capacity to be present? By practicing.

In mindfulness or meditation practices, breathing is key. A daily practice—starting with two to five minutes and building on it—is key. During this exercise, pay attention to your experience of breathing.

Begin by sitting upright in a chair, legs uncrossed, feet flat on the floor. Relax your neck and shoulders; rest your arms by your sides (palms can be facing upward or downward).

Breathe long and gently through your nose, letting the air flow into your belly until you see it gently rise, for a slow count of five. Pause, and hold your breath for a count of five, then exhale through your mouth for another count of five. While doing this, try to clear your mind of all other thoughts.

Repeat this breathing cycle eight to ten times. Each time, practice focusing on your breath and clearing your mind of other thoughts. Remember, it's a practice. Thoughts will come and go. It will get easier.

Another quick way to practice being present is to periodically stop and smile throughout the day. When you smilte, become aware of the immediate physiological response in your body. How does it feel?

We lose a lot of our life experience when we stop being aware. Practice being aware by pausing to notice throughout the day.

Take out a pen and a piece of blank paper. In the next two minutes, write down the negative thoughts, worries, and problems that are on your mind.

_____

_____

_____

_____

_____

_____

_____

_____

_____

_____

_____

_____

_____

_____

_____

_____

_____

_____

_____

_____

_____

_____

_____

_____

_____

_____

_____

_____

_____

_____

_____

_____

Having piled all your thoughts down on your paper, put this paper in a drawer, shut the drawer, and step away. Can you let things be for now? The less you worry about these internal distractions, the easier it will be for you to stay focused on the present moment.

Next, try to replace these thoughts, worries and problems with positive thoughts. Positive thinking allows you to approach life's challenges with a more positive outlook and is helpful in managing stress and enhancing your ability to stay present. Positive thinking has also been shown to enhance your health and wellbeing.

_____

_____

_____

_____

_____

_____

_____

_____

_____

_____

_____

_____

_____

CONTEMPLATION AND JOURNALING

What are you experiencing in this moment?

_____

_____

_____

_____

_____

_____

_____

_____

_____

What are you feeling in this moment?

_____

_____

_____

_____

_____

_____

_____

_____

Now ask yourself: Are you focused on this moment or is your mind wandering? Can you bring it back to the present moment? One way to do so is to take a deep breath and hold it while noticing and naming five things that you can see, feel, hear or smell in the present moment.

8. Cultivating Self-Awareness

"There are three things extremely hard:
steel, a diamond, and to know one's self."
—Benjamin Franklin

Do you know yourself?

It sounds like a ridiculous question with an obvious answer. But if you take one step back, are you really clear about your strengths, your weaknesses, your intentions, and your goals? The only way to have a clear path and a clear purpose is to truly be able to see ourselves.

It's not easy to look in a mirror. We may not always like what we see. But a necessary step in cultivating self-awareness is seeing ourselves clearly—understanding who we are, how others see us, how we see ourselves, and how we fit into the world around us. It is important to undertake this assessment without judgement. We cannot beat ourselves up for mistakes we've made or things we could have done better. Instead, we must see our complete person, accepting any negatives as the simple cost of being human.

One way to cultivate self awareness it to keep a journal. Writing down your thoughts helps you process them more easily and feel more connected and at peace with yourself. Writing can also create more headspace as your words flow out of your mind and onto the paper. Purging your thoughts will help you to get them out of your head and allow you to look at them more objectively.

Another way to become more self aware is to ask for feedback. Feedback allows you to learn more about yourself and how others perceive you.

CONTEMPLATION AND JOURNALING

What's your biggest strength?

_____

_____

_____

_____

_____

_____

_____

_____

What's your biggest weakness?

_____

_____

_____

_____

_____

_____

_____

What is working well in your life today?

_____

_____

_____

_____

_____

_____

_____

_____

_____

What motivates you to make progress?

_____

_____

_____

_____

_____

_____

_____

_____

What makes you stressed?

_____

_____

_____

_____

_____

_____

_____

_____

What relaxes you?

_____

_____

_____

_____

_____

_____

_____

_____

What makes you happy?

_____

_____

_____

_____

_____

_____

_____

_____

What makes you sad?

_____

_____

_____

_____

_____

_____

What makes you angry?

_____

_____

_____

_____

_____

_____

What's your definition of success?

_____

_____

_____

_____

_____

_____

_____

What's your biggest dream or goal?

_____

_____

_____

_____

_____

_____

_____

_____

What obstacles are in the way of that dream?

_____

_____

_____

_____

_____

_____

_____

_____

These questions are not meant to be a fully exhaustive list of things to consider on your journey toward becoming more self-aware. Instead, they are meant as a catalyst to spur on your process of self-discovery.

9. Don't Skimp on Self-Care

"Caring for myself is not self-infuldence, it's self-preservation."
—Audre Lorde

G iven the relentless pace of business today, work-life balance has become a myth. "Work-life integration" is a newer concept that creates more synergies between all areas of one's life: work, family, community, health, and personal well-being. Work-life integration is the first step in acknowledging that it's not a tug-of-war between two areas of our lives: It's a free-for-all with the many facets of our lives we are simultaneously juggling. Still, the mere existence of a new buzzword doesn't make putting that practice into action any easier.

In an increasingly busy world, self-care is absolutely critical not only for success but for survival. And self-care doesn't just mean candles and bubble baths. It's about asking ourselves what we need—emotionally, spiritually, physically—at any given moment.

Here are a few things you can do on a regular basis to prioritize your self-care:

- **Stay attuned to your energy levels**. Today, we are under constant pressure to work longer and harder, often leaving us with an energy lull. Learn to quickly recognize when your energy is getting low so that you can take steps to recharge.

- **Get enough sleep.** We are sleep-deprived as a society. Sleep is essential in helping your body to restore and rejuvenate itself. Adults need to aim for seven to eight hours per night.

- **Build restoration breaks into your day.** Taking a ten-minute walk in nature or a five-minute breathing break can make a big difference.

- **Get rid of processed and high-sugar foods.** Eating lean sources of protein and good fats (such as olive oil and avocado) plus fresh vegetables and fruits will help you to keep your energy balanced throughout the day so that you will have more clarity of mind.

- **Move your body.** Do what you enjoy: walking, running, yoga, pilates, swimming—anything to move for at least 30 minutes per day five days per week. You'll feel better, as exercise improves your cognition and releases endorphins (the "feel-good" hormones).

- **Breathe.** Deep breathing activates the parasympathetic nervous system and helps you to be calmer and more relaxed.

- **Meditate.** Meditation allows you to focus your attention in a way that calms your mind. It's a valuable skill in our 24/7 world as it helps you to be more grounded and more present and to better manage the pace of society today. Even five to ten minutes of meditation per day can be beneficial for your overall health and well-being.

- **Develop a gratitude practice.** Practicing gratitude is an act of self care because it shifts your mindset from one of scarcity to one of abundance. This practice does not have to be overly involved. At the end of each day, write down three people, places or things you are grateful about from the day. Reflect upon why they were meaningful to you. Over time, you will develop a long gratitude list!

- **Spend time alone.** We all have constant demands on our time. Spending 20-30 minutes per day alone in prayer, meditation, reflection, or doing something that you enjoy will help you to manage stress better, be more creative, and problem solve. Spending time alone will also help you to show up better in relationships.

When do you make time to unplug during the week?

_____

_____

_____

_____

_____

_____

_____

_____

Create a list of 5 favorite activities that generate excitement and enhance your ability to unplug and relax.

1.

_____

_____

_____

_____

_____

_____

_____

2.

3.

4.

_____
_____
_____
_____
_____
_____
_____
_____

5.
_____
_____
_____
_____
_____
_____
_____
_____

Think about your daily rhythm. Do you know when to stop, re-evaluate, and recharge?

Yes ☐   No ☐

_____
_____

_____

_____

_____

_____

_____

_____

_____

_____

Do you actively incorporate movement into your routine?

Yes ☐   No ☐

_____

_____

_____

_____

_____

_____

_____

_____

_____

Do you eat only when you are hungry?

Yes ☐   No ☐

_____

_____

_____

_____

_____

_____

_____

Do you eat healthy foods?

Yes ☐   No ☐

_____

_____

_____

_____

_____

_____

_____

Do you sleep 7 -8 hours per night?

Yes ☐   No ☐

Do you feel well-rested during the day?

Yes ☐   No ☐

Are there parts of your life that are out of balance?

Yes ☐   No ☐

Are you willing to address them in order to recharge?

Yes ☐   No ☐

_____

_____

_____

_____

_____

_____

Do you have reliable resources to support you in doing so?

Yes ☐   No ☐

_____

_____

_____

_____

_____

_____

_____

_____

(If you answered 'No' to any or all of the questions above, think about how you may be able to modify aspecits or your life to ensure that you are caring for yourself in key areas including movement, nutrition, sleep, and stress management. What support do you need to do so successfully? Are you willing to get the support that you need in order to prioritize self-care?)

What are you grateful for in your life? List five things that come to mind and reflect on each one for a few minutes.

1.

_____

_____

_____

_____

_____

_____

_____

2.

_____

_____

_____

_____

_____

_____

_____

3.

4.

5.

_____

_____

_____

_____

_____

_____

TRY THIS IN TWO MINUTES: SCHEDULE "ME TIME"

Create a calendar that includes time each day for you to relax and unwind. Plug in at least two blocks of time (15-45 minutes each block) for "Me Time" that complement the blocks of time for work or family commitments. After a week, assess your physical and mental state. How does it feel to take the time during your busy week to care for yourself?

Self-care is one strategy that will help you to avoid burnout. Consider a mini-self-care retreat once per month in which you just focus on you and do things for a few hours that offer you relaxation, comfort or joy. Read a book. Take a walk. Take a bath. Treat yourself to a massage. Go to a class and learn something new. You deserve it.

10. Enlightened Leadership

"If your actions inspire others to dream more, learn more, do more
and become more, you are a leader."
—John Quincy Adams

G iven the rapid pace of societal change, the scope of challenges in
our world today, and the accelerating expansion of the future,
we need enlightened leaders. What is an enlightened leader? When faced
with challenges, an enlightened leader looks at his or her own internal
capacity and evaluates the ways in which he needs to develop his own
inner qualities to successfully meet those challenges. Enlightened leaders
choose authenticity by cultivating the ability to be imperfect and
allowing themselves to be vulnerable. Enlightened leaders maintain
alignment between what they feel and need, and what they say and do.

They also make decisions and choices that are aligned with their core values (I go into more depth on this in Chapter 8 of *Beyond the Mat*).

There are twelve prominent characteristics of enlightened leaders. Enlightened leaders are:

COMPASSIONATE. Enlightened leaders understand the needs of others and put those needs above their own.

COMPETENT. Enlightened leaders understand their strengths and can acknowledge their weaknesses. They are continually learning and evolving.

COURAGEOUS. Enlightened leaders have a strong sense of duty and are not afraid to go against the status quo.

HUMBLE. Enlightened leaders are secure in their identity and lead without arrogance. They value the opinions and contributions of others and seek their engagement.

INTENTIONAL. Enlightened leaders take deliberate action to communicate their vision and mission. They take ownership of their decisions, regardless of whether they succeed or fail.

OPEN-MINDED. Enlightened leaders can see things from different perspectives. They are open to the beliefs and ideas of others.

PASSIONATE. Enlightened leaders have a strong passion for their work. They put their heart and soul into it and are deeply committed through all circumstances, even the most difficult ones.

PURPOSEFUL. Enlightened leaders influence others through their deep sense of purpose and promote an ethical value system to foster an organizational culture with meaning.

SELF-AWARE. Enlightened leaders have an awareness of themselves and others, are tuned in to their emotional state, and recognize how their actions are perceived by others.

SELF-CARING. Enlightened leaders practice self-care so that they are best able to lead others. They also encourage self-care for those they lead.

SPIRITUAL. Enlightened leaders contemplate the principles of their own faith and lead with altruism, hope, and a commitment to make a difference in the lives of others.

VISIONARY. Enlightened leaders ask, *How can I make the world a better place?* Their vision is focused on people and helping to make a better world.

Are you an enlightened leader? Working through the chapters in this self-study guide will help you to become one—a leader who works from the inside out and who operates from a place of authenticity.

<u>CONTEMPLATION AND JOURNALING</u>

Are you comfortable in your own skin or are there aspects of yourself that you are uncomfortable with? If so, how can you shift your mindset or change the things that make you uncomfortable?

_____

_____

_____

_____

_____

_____

_____

_____

In what ways are you emotionally agile?

_____

_____

_____

_____

_____

_____

_____

_____

_____

_____

Do you show compassion to others in your actions and words? How?

_____

_____

_____

_____

_____

_____

_____

_____

_____

What do you stand for? Do you live and act with a deep sense of purpose? How? (Refer back to your personal purpose statement from Chapter 1 if necessary)

_____

_____

_____

_____

_____

_____

_____

_____

_____

What are your biggest fears? How have you/will you face them and overcome them?

_____

_____

_____

_____

_____

_____

_____

_____

Do you recognize the importance of prioritizing self-care? In what ways do you practice self-care? Are you willing to augment your self-care practices in support of your health and wellbeing?

_____

_____

_____

As a leader, how far are you willing to go to make your vision a reality?

11. Celebrate You

"The more you praise and celebrate your life,
the more there is in life to celebrate."
—Oprah Winfrey

Because life's journey isn't easy, it's important to celebrate yourself. But when was the last time you stopped to celebrate yourself?

In our fast-paced and overly busy world, we are constantly doing. We are taught that accomplishment means getting as much done each day as we possibly can. We are focused on the end result rather than the journey. We often lose sight of the present moment. As a result, our pace has become so frenetic that we seldom stop to celebrate ourselves.

If you don't celebrate yourself, who will? And it is critical, as the benefits are plentiful. Celebration of yourself will lead to:

A greater sense of accomplishment through an appreciation of the journey.

A better ability to appreciate and savor the present moment.

Improved self-confidence. Most of us have self-limiting beliefs. By reminding ourselves each day of who we are and what we have accomplished, we rid ourselves of such beliefs and radiate more confidence. When we are confident, it inspires others to become more confident too!

Pride in who you are and what you have accomplished.

If you are having trouble thinking of things that might qualify as "everyday victories" that you may want to celebrate, here's a list of ten small accomplishments to consider:

- Waking up early to exercise.
- Finding the humor in a challenging situation.
- Learning something new.
- Making a stranger smile.
- Spending quality time with family.
- Making a home-coooked meal.
- Cleaning the house.
- Performing a random act of kindness.
- Making time to volunteer.
- Purging your closet and donating old clothes to charity.

How do you celebrate yourself?

_____

_____

_____

_____

_____

_____

_____

_____

What were your three biggest accomplishments in the past year?

_____

_____

_____

_____

_____

_____

_____

_____

What were the most memorable moments that you had on the journey to achieving these accomplishments?

_____

_____

_____

_____

_____

_____

_____

_____

Write a gratitude letter to yourself. You may have taken time to express your gratitude to others, but have you invested time in looking at what you are grateful for in yourself. Do so now – why wait?

Dear Me,

I am grateful to you because of who you are for the following reasons:

_____

_____

_____

_____

_____

_____

_____

_____

_____

<u>Try this in two minutes: Celebrate Life</u>

As part of your morning routine, spend one minute each day celebrating your life and one minute writing a few thoughts down about your experience. After practicing for a week, take time to reflect. Did you experience a shift in your mindset? If yes, how? Does this practice help you to experience a sense of joy and fulfillment?

When you take time to acknowledge the actions that supported you in achieving your goals, you strengthen those actions and associate positive emotions with them. Daily acknowledgements become habits that will eventually start coming naturally to you each and every day.

Conclusion

"The privilege of a lifetime is to become who you truly are."
—Carl Jung

When we live authentically, our actions and words are aligned with our beliefs and values. Being true—becoming your authentic self—will let you make your greatest contribution to the world. You will become more curious, courageous, and confident, and you will in turn inspire others to make their greatest contributions. You

One of my primary goals is to help people to augment their personal leadership skills so that they can lead more healthy and fulfilling lives. Personal leadership is less about what you do and more about who you are and how you become that individual. I hope that this guide has provided you with useful information so that you can live and lead authentically and with joy.

Good luck on your journey! May it be a peaceful and joyful one.

Made in the USA
Las Vegas, NV
26 July 2021

27060635R00069